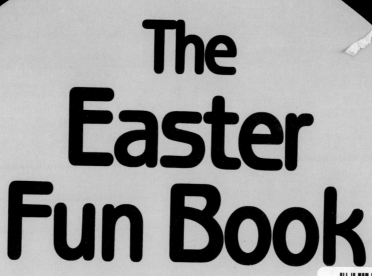

The Easter Fun Book

This book
belongs to:

(Why not draw a picture of yourself here?)

Illustrations
by
Colin Smithson

Text by

Davina and
Lois Rock

A LION BOOK

Hooray for Easter

Easter is a happy time. It's a time to be glad that winter is on the way out. Spring is coming!

Sheep are having lambs.

Chicks are hatching out of eggs.

Flowers have sprouted from bulbs planted in the earth.

The soil is warm and seeds are growing into seedlings.

There is new life everywhere.

Did you know that Easter is a special church festival? Sometimes it seems that life is dull: as dull as a dried-out old seed, a dead-looking branch in winter, or an egg that hasn't hatched. On the first Easter Day, a special person called Jesus showed people that life could be as full of joy as the world in spring.

New Life

Here are lots of springtime arrivals. Draw a line from each new arrival to where it has come from.

The answers are on page 32.

Easter Egg Hunt

An Easter egg hunt is great fun.
All the Easter eggs that you see below
are also hidden somewhere in the big
picture. Put a cross in the box next to
each egg when you find where it has
been hidden!

5

Look Again!

Make your own Easter egg hunt.
As a special Easter treat, hide a small chocolate
egg with each of your card eggs.

You need:

thin card

scissors

felt-tip pens

(1) Draw egg shapes on
pieces of card, then cut
them out. You can copy
the shape shown here if
you like.

(2) Now decorate your
eggs with lots of bright
colours.

(3) Hide your eggs around
the house. Now get your
family to hunt for them!

Decorate an Egg

Here is a design for you to copy.
Why not colour in this design using your
favourite colours?

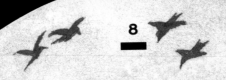

Jesus and the First Easter
Birds and Flowers

Long ago, in the land that is now called Israel, there lived a man called Jesus. Many people wanted to be his friends. He was kind to them, and he spent lots of time talking to them.

'Look at the lovely world around you,' he said to them one day. 'Look at the wild flowers. Aren't they beautiful? And they just grow that way. People work and work so they can buy smart clothes. But even the very rich in their very best clothes don't look as good as these flowers.

'The God who made the world made all these flowers. And if God takes care of flowers, you can be sure God will take care of you.

'And look at the birds flying around. They don't sow any crops. They don't work hard in the fields gathering in the harvest. They don't have anywhere to store their food. But the world provides what they need to eat.

'The God who made the world made all these birds. And if God takes care of birds, you can be sure God will take care of you.'

What's That Called?

Here are some of the wild flowers and birds that are common in the country where Jesus lived – and in many other places. Can you write their names?

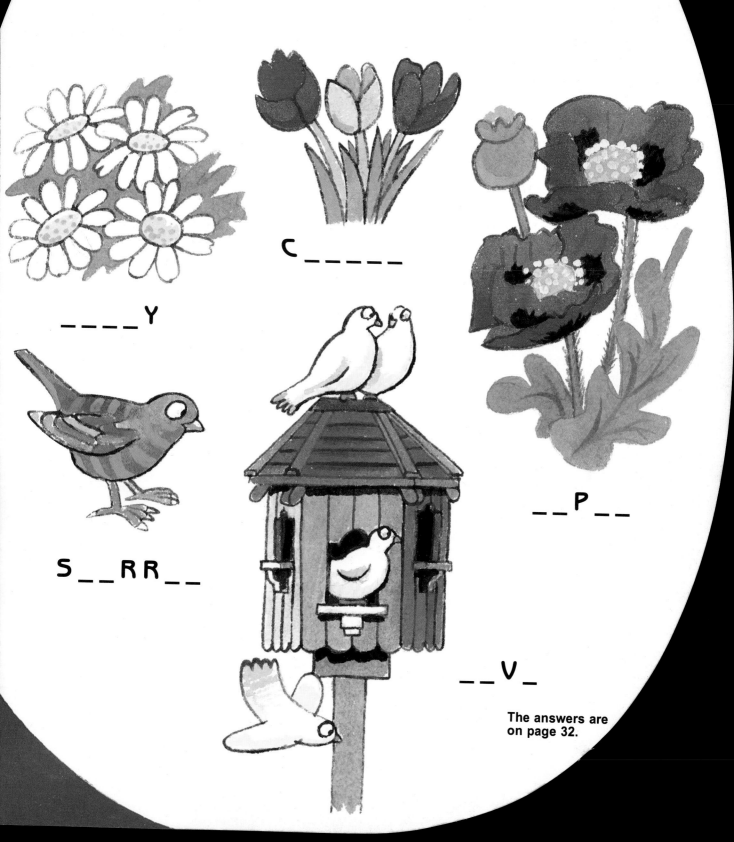

C _ _ _ _ _ _

_ _ _ _ _ Y

S _ _ R R _ _

_ _ P _ _

_ _ V _

The answers are on page 32.

Bright Birds

Make a bird to brighten up your Easter.

Cut smaller squares to make babies for your bird. You can put these on your fingers like puppets . . . and make up chirpy songs for them to sing.

You need:

paper
a pencil
a ruler
felt-tips or crayons
scissors
sticky tape

(1) Draw a square shape on your paper. A big bird needs a square 8cm x 8cm. Cut it out.

(2) Fold the paper in half. Draw this bird design on one side.

(3) Now turn the folded paper over, and draw the same design facing the other way. When you unfold the paper, the drawing looks like the one above.

④ Cut a tail piece.

⑤ Colour your bird. Snip the tail piece to make feathers.

⑥ Tape the tail piece to the back end of the bird.

⑦ Fold in the back corners and tape in place.

⑧ Fold in the front corners to give your bird a pointed beak, and tape in place.

Nesting Time

Many birds make cosy nests where the mother bird can lay her eggs, and where the baby birds can be kept safe and warm.

The baby birds in these nests are waiting for their mum or dad to come back. Can you tell which big bird they are waiting for?

Here's how to make a basket for your bright birds from page 10.

1 Lay the plate on the cardboard and draw a circle. Cut it out.

2 Now mark five notches like this and cut them out.

You need:

a small plate

a piece of cardboard

a pencil

scissors

wool

sticky tape

3 Now tape one end of your wool near the point of one of the notches.

4 Weave the wool over and under, and over and under... round and round and round.

5 Stop weaving when you are about 2cm from the top of the card. Snip the wool and tuck the end into the weaving.

Butterfly Garden

Easter is a good time to sow seeds. Try sowing flower seeds such as marigolds and nasturtiums in a pot of soil. Keep the soil moist, and keep the pot in a place where it gets lots of light. In the summer you will have lovely flowers.

Make some butterflies to dance over your pot while you wait for the flowers to grow.

You need:

a long straw

a piece of paper

felt-tip pens or crayons

scissors

sticky tape

1 Fold the piece of paper in half.

2 Draw a butterfly on the paper so the top of each wing is on the fold.

3 Cut out the butterfly through both layers, leaving the top wingtips joined.

④ Open up the butterfly. Decorate it as beautifully as you can.

⑤ Turn the butterfly to the wrong side, and tape the straw to the body part.

⑥ Now fold the butterfly bright side out, and tape the wings together at the sides.

You can make paper flowers for your pot while you wait for the real seeds to grow.

Pick-Your-Own-Flower

Easter Card

A fun card to give to a friend.

① First fold the card.

You need:

green paper

paper in other bright colours

scissors

sticky tape

a pencil

glue

② On the inside, write: Happy Easter.

③ Now cut the parts of a flower, including a tuft of green leaves for the bottom part.

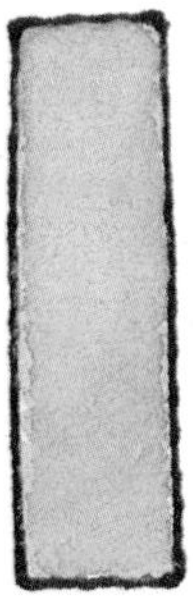

④ Stick the tuft of leaves in place along the sides and bottom.

⑤ Now stick the centre of the flower on its stalk.

⑥ Plant the flower among its tuft of leaves...

⑦ ...and your friend can pick it.

Learn About Lambs

A father sheep is called a ram. Some rams have curly horns. A mother sheep is called a ewe.

A baby sheep is called a lamb. Sometimes ewes have twin lambs – or even triplets!

At first, lambs drink milk from their mother. Soon they learn to nibble grass as well.

A grown up sheep makes a low 'baa' sound. A young lamb makes a high 'maa'.

Jesus and the First Easter
The Sheep and the Shepherd

Jesus was a good friend to all kinds of people. That made some people cross.

'Jesus is a friend to people who do wrong things,' they muttered. 'How dare a man like that tell us about God?'

Jesus decided to tell them a story:

'Does anyone here have sheep?' he asked.

Well, lots of the people he was talking to had sheep. And all of them had seen shepherds looking after their flocks on the rocky hills around them.

'Imagine that a shepherd has one hundred sheep,' said Jesus. 'One day, they are out on the hills. He counts them. There are only ninety-nine.

'What does he do? Of course: he goes looking for the one that is lost. And when he finds it, he's very happy. He puts it on his shoulders and carries it home.

'"Hooray!" he says. "I've found the sheep that was lost."

'And he invites all his friends and neighbours round to celebrate.

'Now, if a shepherd cares for sheep like that . . . imagine how much God cares for people. Imagine the celebration when someone who has done wrong things changes their mind, and wants to live as God's friend.'

Lamb's Puzzle Page

Count the Sheep

How many sheep can you see in this picture?

Home and Away

This lamb likes to explore, and she likes to come home again.

(1) Cut out the lamb on the back cover. Tape one end of a piece of yarn to the lamb, and the other end to the lamb's place with the rest of the flock.

(2) Now take the lamb to look at the poppies. And back.

(3) Now take the lamb to see her friend the sparrow. And back.

(4) Where else does she like to go?

The answers are on page 32.

Jesus and the First Easter
A Very Sad Day

Jesus told people how much God loved them and cared for them. And Jesus showed that he loved people. He talked to them. He told them stories. He shared food with them, and went to parties with them.

And he could do wonderful things. He touched blind people ... and they could see again. He told people who had been unable to walk to get up ... and they could: they could walk and run and dance. He made sick people well.

But some people did not like Jesus. They weren't sure that he was right when he told them about God. And because he was getting so popular, they thought he might cause problems with the people in charge of the country.

It was one of Jesus' friends who let him down. A man named Judas. He told Jesus' enemies where they could find him alone.

They sent men with clubs and swords to take Jesus.

They made him their prisoner.

They took him to the people in charge of the country, the Romans, and told lies about to get him into trouble.

Their plan worked. Although Jesus

had done no wrong, his enemies had him put to death. The way the Romans did this was very cruel. Jesus was nailed to a cross of wood, and left to die.

Jesus was hurting: he was wounded and bleeding.

But Jesus still loved people, just as he had said God loves people. And he spoke to God, a sort of prayer:

'Father,' he said to God, 'forgive them. They don't know what they are doing.'

Soon after, he died. His friends put his body in a stone tomb, like a cave. They rolled the round stone door shut.

Jesus had been loving and kind to the very end.

Winter

Here is a picture of a garden in winter.
The world seems dead.

Spring

What a difference when spring comes!
How many springtime changes can you
see in the garden?

The answers are on page 32.

Jesus and the First Easter
A Very Happy Day

A few days later, some of Jesus' friends went back to the tomb. They wanted to say a proper goodbye to the body of the man who had been their friend.

To their amazement, the stone door was rolled open.

And the tomb was empty.

While they stood there wondering, two people in clothes that gleamed like lightning came and stood next to them.

'Why do you look in a tomb for someone who is alive?' they asked. 'Jesus isn't here. He is risen!'

Soon after, in the garden there. Jesus' friends saw him alive again. For many days afterwards, they saw him in other places too. He told them what he wanted them to do.

'Go and tell people the good news about me,' he said. 'Take care of them, as a good shepherd takes care of sheep.

'I told people about God, and showed them how to live as God wants. And now I am alive again, to show that God will give new life to anyone who follows me.'

Then Jesus went to be with God, to make a home with God for all the people in the world who would follow him.

And that is the good news people celebrate at Easter.

Easter Celebrations

If you go into a church at Easter, you may see some of these special reminders of the story of Jesus.

○A cross. Jesus was dying on a cross when he forgave his enemies.

○An Easter garden. A little model of the hill were Jesus died, the tomb where his friends put his body . . . and the garden where they saw him alive again.

○Flowers. These are a sign of new life springing up out of seeds and bulbs that have been buried in the cold ground . . . and a reminder of Jesus coming back to life after three days buried in a tomb.

Easter Treats

Mr Hen's Famous Recipe

Easter is a happy time! Celebrate by sharing some of these delicious sweets.

(1) Put the two sorts of sugar and the ground almonds into a bowl.

First we wash our hands.

You need:

100g icing sugar

100g caster sugar

200g ground almonds

1 egg

a bowl

a mixing spoon

a teaspoon

(2) Now crack the egg in and mix until you have a stiff paste.

③ Take heaped teaspoons of the mix and roll them to make egg shapes. Then put them into some pretty paper cases.

These make a lovely Easter gift. Try making baskets like the one on pages 30 and 31, and fill them with a few delicious eggs.

Easter Gift

Make Mr Hen's special Easter Treat eggs, and put them in a box, to give as a gift.

You need:

scissors
sticky tape
tissue paper

First the box:

① Cut the box shape from the back cover of this book.

② Fold along the lines as shown, and tape in place.

③ Fold the handles in place.

Now the lining:

④ Cut a square of paper 15cm x 15cm.

⑤ Fold it half, and in half again.

⑥ Cut around the two edges that aren't folded, to make a pattern.

⑦ Unfold the paper, and gently press it into your box to line it.

Make a label and tie it to the basket

⑧ Fill it with Mr Hen's eggs — or some sweets.

Answers

PAGE 3

A daffodil from a bulb, A chick from a hen, A baby rabbit from a mother rabbit, A branch in blossom from a bare branch, A packet of sweets from a chocolate egg

PAGE 9

Crocus, poppy, daisy, sparrow, dove

PAGE 20

There are eleven sheep altogether

PAGE 21

The lamb also likes to visit the ducks by the duck pond

BASKET

Make more baskets like the one on the back cover by copying this shape onto card. Use your favourite crayons or stickers to decorate it before you fold it to make a basket.

PAGES 24 AND 25

(1) The grass is growing
(2) The flowers are in bloom – daisies, daffodils and tulips
(3) The leaves on the tree are coming out
(4) The birds have made a nest for their new family
(5) A butterfly has emerged from a chrysalis
(6) The sun is shining
(7) Mr and Mrs Hen are wearing spring clothes
(8) Mr and Mrs Hen have a new family of chicks
(9) Someone has hidden an Easter egg in the garden!

Copyright © 1995 Lion Publishing
Illustrations copyright © 1995 Colin Smithson

Published by
Lion Publishing plc
Sandy Lane West, Oxford, England
ISBN 0 7459 3100 6

Albatross
Books Pty Ltd
PO Box 320,
Sutherland, NSW,
2232, Australia
ISBN 0 7324 1226 9

First edition 1995

All rights reserved

A catalogue for this book
is available from the British Library

Printed and bound in Italy

A TREASURY
of
SCOTTISH VERSE

To beloved friends,
with love on your
great adventure

Tim & Margaret
xx

DEDICATION for 'Papa'

Editor Fleur Robertson
Design concept Philip Clucas
Design Justina Leitão, Mike Rose
Photography Scotland in Focus Picture Library
Picture research Bob Lawson

Production Ruth Arthur, Karen Staff, Neil Randles
Director of Production Gerald Hughes

Published in Ireland by
Gill & Macmillan Ltd, Goldenbridge, Dublin 8
and associated companies around the world

CLB 4993

This selection and introduction
© 1997 CLB International, Godalming, Surrey

ISBN 0 7171 2617 X

Printed and bound in Singapore

Jacket: Kilchurn Castle, Argyllshire
Previous page: Tarbet, Loch Fyne
Facing page: Loch Long and Ben Killilan

A TREASURY

of

SCOTTISH VERSE

Gill & Macmillan

CONTENTS

INTRODUCTION

*A*lthough this selection of verse and songs by Scottish poets is not solely about Scotland, every page is of Scotland. The unique character of the Scottish, their joy and their sadness, their hopes and aspirations, their deep abiding love of their homeland, shines through in every line. The poems have been chosen for their beauty, their accessibility and their sincerity: the majority are nature poems. As individual as the poets that penned them, they celebrate one of the most varied and interesting countries in Europe, its rivers and lochs, its hills and mountains, its native wildlife and plants in a way that can make these things seem new, even to those who know them well.

Presented alongside a superb selection of photographs, the verses have been chosen to illuminate and enrich both the visitor to Scotland and those who have lived here all their lives. Pride in one's home and a strong sense of place are frequent themes, and few who have seen even a small number of the many landscapes and seascapes Scotland contains could deny this is a country of which to be proud, in which to delight, indeed. When all is said and done, this poetry is celebratory – and of a place worth the celebration.

Facing page: Pass of the Cattle, Kishorn, Wester Ross

WESTERING HOME

Chorus

And it's westering home, and a song in the air,
Light in the eye, and it's goodbye to care.
Laughter o' love, and a welcoming there,
Isle of my heart, my own one.

Tell me o' lands o' the Orient gay,
Speak o' the riches and joys o' Cathay;
Eh, but it's grand to be wakin' ilk day
To find yourself nearer to Isla.

Where are the folk like the folk o' the west?
Canty, and couthy, and kindly, the best.
There I would hie me and there I would rest
At hame wi' my ain folk in Isla.

ANONYMOUS

Right: Sunset over Laggan Bay, Islay,
Inner Hebrides

LOCH BRANDY

All day I hear the water talk
From dripping rock to rock
And water in bright snowflakes scatter
On boulders of the black Whitewater;
But louder now than these
The silent scream of the loose tumbling screes.

Grey wave on grey stone hits
And grey moth flits
Moth after moth, but oh,
What floats into that silver glow,
What golden moth
That rises with a strange majestic sloth?

O heart, why tremble with desire
As on the water shakes that bridge of fire?
The gold moth floats away, too soon
To narrow to a hard white moon
That scarce will light the path
Stumbling to where the cold mist wreaths the strath.

ANDREW YOUNG

Facing page: Loch Brandy, Glen Clova, Angus

THE FISHERMAN

As he comes from one of those small houses
Set within the curve of the low cliff
For a moment he pauses
Foot on step at the low lintel
Before fronting the wind and sun.
He carries out from within something of the dark
Concealed by heavy curtain,
Or held within the ship under hatches.

Yet with what assurance
The compact body moves,
Head pressed to wind,
His being at an angle
As to anticipate the lurch of earth.

Who is he to contain night
And still walk stubborn
Holding the ground with light feet
And with a careless gait?

Perhaps a cataract of light floods,
Perhaps the apostolic flame.
Whatever it may be
The road takes him from us.
Now the pier is his, now the tide.

GEORGE BRUCE

Facing page: Craighouse Pier, Jura, Inner Hebrides

FREEDOM OF THE HILLS

*M*ine is the freedom of the tranquil hills
When vagrant breezes bend the sinewy grass,
While sunshine on the widespread landscape spills
And light as down the fleet cloud-shadows pass.

Mine, still, that freedom when the storm clouds race,
Cracking their whips against defiant crags
And mists swirl boiling up from inky space
To vanish on the instant, torn to rags.

When winter grips the mountain in a vice,
Silently stifling with its pall of snow,
Checking the streams, clasping the rocks in ice,
Still to the mantled summits I would go.

Sun-drenched, I sense the message they impart,
Storm-lashed, I hear it sing through every vein;
Among the snows it whispers to my heart
'Here is your freedom. Taste – and come again!'

DOUGLAS FRASER

Right: River Runie and Loch Broom, Wester Ross

THE FALLS OF FALLOCH

*T*his white explosion of water plunges down
With the deep-voiced rush of sound that shakes a city.
A fine cold smoke drifts across dripping stone
And wet black walls of rock shut in the scene.

Now thought hangs sheer on a precipice of beauty
Lifting with leaping water out from the rock.
A gasp of time, flung clear in a weight of falling,
Bursts like a bud above the deep pool's black
Parted and curled back under by the shock
Where light's bright spark dives to the dark's controlling.

But the brilliance is not extinguished. The heart leaps up,
The heart of the fall leaps up, an eternal explosion,
Force without spending, form without fetter of shape.
And at the pool's edge wavelets scarcely lap
Where drifted spume clings with a soft adhesion.

SYDNEY TREMAYNE

Facing page: Mountain waterfall

CALEDONIA

O Caledonia! stern and wild
Meet nurse for a poetic child!
Land of brown heath and shaggy wood,
Land of the mountain and the flood,
Land of my sires! what mortal hand
Can e'er untie the filial band,
That knits me to thy rugged strand!
Still, as I view each well-known scene,
Think what is now, and what hath been,
Seems as, to me, of all bereft,
Sole friends thy woods and streams were left;
And thus I love them better still,
Even in extremity of ill.
By Yarrow's stream still let me stray,
Though none should guide my feeble way;
Still feel the breeze down Ettricke break,
Although it chill my withered cheek;
Still lay my head by Teviot stone,
Though there, forgotten and alone,
The Bard may draw his parting groan.

SIR WALTER SCOTT

Right: Upper Glen Nevis, Lochaber

THE PERMANENCE
OF THE YOUNG MEN

*N*o man outlives the grief of war
   Though he outlive its wreck:
Upon the memory a scar
   Through all his years will ache.

Hope will revive when horrors cease;
   And dreaming dread be stilled;
But there shall dwell within his peace
   A sadness unannulled.

Upon his world shall hang a sign
   Which summer cannot hide:
The permanence of the young men
   Who are not by his side.

WILLIAM SOUTER

Right: The Commando Memorial,
Spean Bridge, Lochaber

THE MOUNTAIN

*T*he burn ran blacker for snow
And ice-floe on ice-floe
Jangled in heavy lurches
Beneath the claret-coloured birches.

Dark grouse rose becking from the ground
And deer turned sharp heads round,
The antlers on their brows
Like stunted trees with withered boughs.

I climbed to where the mountain sloped
And long wan bubbles groped
Under the ice's cover,
A bridge that groaned as I crossed over.

I reached the mist, brighter than day,
That showed a specious way
By narrow crumbling shelves,
Where rocks grew larger than themselves.

But when I saw the mountain's spire
Looming through that damp fire,
I left it still unwon
And climbed down to the setting sun.

ANDREW YOUNG

Facing page: Buchaille Etive Mhor,
Glencoe, Lochaber

THE WOOD AND THE SHORE

The low bay melts into a ring of silver,
And slips it on the shore's reluctant finger.
Though in an hour the tide will turn, will tremble,
Forsaking her because the moon persuades him.
But the black wood that leans and sighs above her
No hour can change, no moon can slave or summon.
Then comes the dark; on sleepy, shell-strewn beaches,
O'er long, pale leagues of sand, and cold clear water
She hears the tide go out towards the moonlight.
The wood still leans ... weeping she turns to seek him
And his black hair all night is on her bosom.

MURIEL STUART

Right: Applecross Bay, Wester Ross

ANEMONES

*A*nemones, they say, are out
   By sheltered woodland streams,
With budding branches all about
   Where Spring-time sunshine gleams;

Such are the haunts they love, but I
   With swift remembrance see
Anemones beneath a sky
   Of cold austerity –

Pale flowers too faint for winds so chill
   And with too fair a name –
That day I lingered on a hill
   For one who never came.

MARION ANGUS

Facing page: Wood Anemone

SUN BLINK

On a steaming cloud the sun jumps,
                          crowing light,
And the air opens like a book. Its blinding
Pages are stained with grass suddenly green
And water suddenly blue. Bracken is sending

Messages by mirrors, to anywhere,
Under the hawk that hangs like an apostle
Over his own bad news. The water rings
Clearer than coins. And with a whispering
                          whistle

This heather clump that's forest to my head
Swarms in a mile of blue ... Time stirs his fire,
And here and everywhere begins to write
Another paragraph on the opened air.

NORMAN MACCAIG

Right: Ben More and Loch Scridain,
Isle of Mull, Inner Hebrides

STRAWBERRIES

There were never strawberries
like the ones we had
that sultry afternoon
sitting on the step
of the open french window
facing each other
your knees held in mine
the blue plates on our laps
the strawberries glistening
in the hot sunlight
we dipped them in sugar
looking at each other
not hurrying the feast
for one to come
the empty plates
laid on the stone together
with the two forks crossed

and I bent towards you
sweet in that air
in my arms
abandoned like a child
from your eager mouth
the taste of strawberries
in my memory
lean back again
let me love you
let the sun beat
on our forgetfulness
one hour of all
the heat intense
and summer lightning
on the Kilpatrick hills

let the storm wash the plates

EDWIN MORGAN

Facing page: Scottish strawberries

THE TRAVELLER HAS REGRETS

The traveller has regrets
For the receding shore
That with its many nets
Has caught, not to restore,
The white lights in the bay,
The blue lights on the hill,
Though night with many stars
May travel with him still,
But night has nought to say,
Only a colour and shape
Changing like cloth shaking,
A dancer with a cape
Whose dance is heart-breaking,
Night with its many stars
Can warn travellers
There's only time to kill
And nothing much to say:
But the blue lights on the hill,
The white lights in the bay
Told us the meal was laid
And that the bed was made
And that we could not stay.

G.S. FRASER

Right: Portree harbour
at dusk, Isle of Skye,
Inner Hebrides

THE SUFFICIENT PLACE

*S*ee, all the silver roads wind in, lead in
To this still place like evening. See, they come
Like messengers bearing gifts to this little house,
And this great hill worn down to a patient mound,
And these tall trees whose motionless branches bear
An aeon's summer foliage, leaves so thick
They seem to have robbed a world of shade, and kept
No room for all these birds that line the boughs
With heavier riches, leaf and bird and leaf.
Within the doorway stand
Two figures, Man and Woman, simple and clear
As a child's first images. Their manners are
Such as were known before the earliest fashion
Taught the Heavens guile. The room inside is like
A thought that needed thus much space to write on,
Thus much, no more. Here all's sufficient. None
That comes complains, and all the world comes here,
Comes, and goes out again, and comes again.
This is the Pattern, these the Archetypes,
Sufficient, strong and peaceful. All outside
From end to end of the world is tumult. Yet
These roads do not turn in here but writhe on
Round the wild earth for ever. If a man
Should chance to find this place three times in time
His eyes are changed and make a summer silence
Amid the tumult, seeing the road wind in
To their still home, the house and the leaves and birds.

EDWIN MUIR

Right: Croft house,
Glen Etive, Argyllshire

FOR THE OLD HIGHLANDS

That old lonely lovely way of living
in Highland places, – twenty years a-growing,
twenty-years flowering, twenty years declining, –
father to son, mother to daughter giving
ripe tradition; peaceful bounty flowing;
one harmony all tones of life combining, –
old wise ways, passed like the dust blowing.

The harmony of folk and land is shattered, –
the yearly rhythm of things, the social graces,
peat-fire and music, candle-light and kindness.
Now they are gone it seems they never mattered,
much, to the world, those proud and violent races,
clansmen, and chiefs whose passioned greed and blindness
made desolate these lovely lonely places.

DOUGLAS YOUNG

Left: Pass of Glencoe from Lochan na Fola, Lochaber

TROUT FISHER

*S*emphill, his hat stuck full of hooks
    Sits drinking ale
        Among the English fishing visitors,
    Probes in detail
        Their faults in casting, reeling, selection of flies.
'Never,' he urges, 'do what it says in the books.'
        Then they, obscurely wise,
        Abandon by the loch their dripping oars
    And hang their throttled tarnish on the scale.

'Forgive me, every speckled trout,'
    Says Semphill then,
        'And every swan and eider on these waters.
    Certain strange men,
        Taking advantage of my poverty
Have wheedled all my subtle loch-craft out
        So that their butchery
        Seems fine technique in the ear of wives and daughters;
    And I betray the loch for a white coin.'

GEORGE MACKAY BROWN

Right: Trout fishing on Lindores Loch, Fife

Woodland path

44
~

A BIRTHDAY

I never felt so much
Since I have felt at all
The tingling smell and touch
Of dogrose and sweet briar,
Nettles against the wall,
All sours and sweets that grow
Together or apart
In hedge or marsh or ditch.
I gather to my heart
Beast, insect, flower, earth, water, fire,
In absolute desire,
As fifty years ago.

Acceptance, gratitude:
The first look and the last
When all between has passed
Restore ingenuous good
That seeks no personal end
Nor strives to mar or mend.
Before I touched the food
Sweetness ensnared my tongue;
Before I saw the wood
I loved each nook and bend,
The track going right and wrong;
Before I took the road
Direction ravished my soul.
Now that I can discern
It whole or almost whole,
Acceptance and gratitude
Like travellers return
And stand where first they stood.

EDWIN MUIR

THE ISLAND

When we reached the island
it was evening
and we were at peace,
the sun lying down
under the sea's quilt
and the dream beginning anew.

But in the morning
we tossed the cover aside
and in that white light
saw a loch in the island,
and an island in the loch,
and we recognized
that the dream had moved away from us again.

The stepping-stones are chancy
to the second island,
the stone totters
that guards the berries,
the rowan withers,
we have lost now the scent of the honeysuckle.

DERICK THOMSON

Right: Dawn over Loch Earn, Perthshire

HIGHLAND SHOOTING LODGE

Crouched up beneath a crowd of Grampian hills,
this old house waits to hear the report of guns
crisping the Autumn air, for its rooms again
to warm to the jokes of August-trampling men
roughed by the grasp and snap of salmon gills,
the twisted necks of grouse. But nobody comes.

Only, at times, a shapeless horde of cloud
that shifts about the rocky peaks, creeps down
to lick at gutters soured with rotting leaves,
or rub a shapeless back against cold eaves,
then vanish, thin as breath; the drifting shroud
of everything men once had thought they owned.

MAURICE LINDSAY

Facing page: Canisp from Suileag Bothy,
Lochinver, Sutherland

FROST ROUND THE HOUSE

There is no sound under the frost.
Tonight it is as though the walls are frozen too
So intense is this silence, this stillness.
Nothing moves at all
And I wonder,
What sounds usually fill the evenings
When winter and darkness bend houses to the earth?
Usually there is sound or I wouldn't notice the lack.
There is no creak of a robbing wind unwary on rafters
No sound of a window's struggle.
There is no murmur from outside from the deeps
                              of the tumbled burn
No muted mutter of trees and waves.
There is no sound.
All round the house the night sits hunched as an owl
Feathered and still
But more still than the night,
Inside the house
Is the curious listening of the air –
Yet
There is no sound to hear.

ANNE MURRAY

Right: Winter near Delnabo, Tomintoul, Banffshire

HIGHLAND PORTRAIT

Castles draw in their horns. The stones are streaming
with fine Highland rain. A woman's struggling
against the sour wet wind in a black skirt.
Mist on the mountains. Waterfalls are pouring
their tons of water with a hollow roaring.
The phantom chieftains pass the heavy port.

Fences straggle westwards. Absurd cattle
lift their shaggy heads through humming water.
A duck dives coolly into stylish seas.
Hotels are sleeping in their winter colours.
The oil skinned sailors wear their gleaming yellows.
Glencoes are wailing in the hollow trees.

Country of céilidhs and the delicate manners,
obstinate dowagers of emerald honours,
the rain has worn your metaphors away.
Only poor rays of similes are shining
from brooches and from buckles. The complaining
barren rocks and ravens fill the day.

Nothing to say except a world has ended.
The waters of Polldubh, direct and splendid,
will hump unsteady men to a boiling death.
Yet from the shaking bridge of fascination
we see in these the antiseptic passion
whose surgeon's reason is a kind of birth.

IAIN CRICHTON SMITH

Left: Kilchurn Castle and Loch Awe, Argyllshire

THE CLEARING

*W*oodsmoke, sheer grapebloom, smears
The trunks of trees, tricks larches
Lilac, and as deftly clears.
Startlingly, among patches

Of sunlight, come glints
Of steel: the woodmen are at it
Early. Red-jerkined, gigantic
In quirk lighting, they flit

Under branches, make markings
Or, smirched, become blurs
Of themselves. Somewhere a dog barks.
Hand-saws spark, and sputter.

Breaking cover, a brood
Of partridges wheedles
Through charlock. Lopped wood
Crippling down, sends needles

Showering. Blades whirr; logs are
Rolled and chained. Crushed
Brushwood leaks. Air
Is spiced with resin and sawdust.

Then they are gone, to the sound
Of singing. Where pathways join,
Fires flicker. And the ground
Is littered with huge copper coins.

STEWART CONN

Right: Beech woodland in Perthshire

Mute swans

WATCHING YOU WALK

*W*atching you walk slowly across a stage,
Suddenly I am become aware of all the past;
Of all the tragic maids and queens of every age,
Of Joan, whose love the flames could not arrest.

Of those to whom always love was the first duty,
Who saw behind the crooked world the ugly and weak,
Whose kindliness was no gesture; no condescending pity
Could rule their actions; those whom Time broke,

But whom he could not totally destroy.
Hearing the truth you give to these dead words,
Whose writer feared the life they might enjoy,
I can recall the mating orchestra of birds

Behind your voice, as lying by the lake,
You read me Owen, and I, too deeply moved,
Watched the swans for a moment, before I spoke
The trivialities, unable to tell you how I loved.

Watching your fingers curl about a painted death,
I am suddenly glad that it is April, that you are queen
Of all the sordid marches of my bruised heart,
That, loving you, the poplars never seemed to green.

Glad of my lonely walk beside the sunken river,
Thinking of you while seeing the tufts of ash,
The chestnut candles and unreal magnolia's wax flower;
Glad that, in loving you, the whole world lives afresh.

RUTHVEN TODD

THE FALLS OF GLOMACH

Rain drifts forever in this place
  Tossed from the long white lace
  The Falls trail on the black rocks below,
  And golden-rod and rose root shake
  In wind that they forever make;
  So though they wear their own rainbow
  It's not in hope, but just for show,
  For rain and wind together
  Here through the summer make a chill wet weather.

ANDREW YOUNG

Right: Waterfall and wild flowers

ON LOOKING AT AN
OLD CLIMBING PHOTOGRAPH

I have been there
    High on that rock perch. Beneath my feet
    A thousand feet of air
    And far below the moor spread like a map,
    The mountains crowding round
    Waiting to hear the roll-call of their names:
    Some, valued friends recalling splendid climbs,
    Some still to meet, sending their challenge out
    For future days.

    We felt like giants, sitting there at ease
    With half of Scotland in our view,
    Though hours before
    We seemed as insignificant as ants
    As we peered upwards at those mighty crags.
    Yet slowly we advanced,
    Muscles responding as the need arose
    Effort and craft achieved their goal at last
    And that reward
    Which climbers know but cannot well explain.
    What need – so long as they can climb again?

DOUGLAS FRASER

Facing page: Beinn Liath Mhor
Fannaich, Wester Ross

PRINCES STREET GARDENS

The long paved walk is parallel to the street.
Traffic is silenced in the still air
of this amphitheatre below street level.
Listen to your footfalls on the flagstones
and feel yourself beginning to relax.
The place persuades. Along the walk
old men alleviate their loneliness
and share their misremembered memories;
fat mums prise shoes from swollen feet.
And no one stares, for nothing is out of place.
Nuns with cameras laugh openly, aloud;
a blonde girl turns to her lover, smiles
and presses his black hand to her pale cheek
and no one stares, for nothing is out of place.
Year after year these images recur
in this amphitheatre of still air.
Your eyes grow charitable, the place persuades.

JAMES AITCHISON

Right: The Scott Memorial and East Princes
Street Gardens, Edinburgh

TODD

*M*y father's white uncle became
Arthritic and testamental in
Lyrical stages. He held cardinal sin
Was misuse of horses, then any game

Won on the sabbath. A Clydesdale
To him was not bells and sugar or declension
From paddock, but primal extension
Of rock and soil. Thundered nail

Turned to sacred bolt. And each night
In the stable he would slaver and slave
At cracked hooves, or else save
Bowls of porridge for just the right

Beast. I remember I lied
To him once, about oats: then I felt
The brand of his loving tongue, the belt
Of his own horsey breath. But he died,

When the mechanised tractor came to pass.
Now I think of him neighing to some saint
In a simple heaven or, beyond complaint,
Leaning across a fence and munching grass.

STEWART CONN

Facing page: Lunging a young horse

ON THE CLIFF

Earth with my little pathway ends
   Abruptly, and I stand
Where in a wall of snow extends
   The breakage of the land.

White birds, like fragments of the cliff,
   Fly on the empty air,
Crying as though from hearts made stiff
   With straitening despair.

And far beneath me on the beach
   Sings the incessant sea,
And sighs like love that cannot reach
   To Love's eternity.

Lord, in the weakness of my words
   Let all these pray for me,
The broken cliff, the crying birds
   And the foam-mottled sea.

ANDREW YOUNG

Left: Bullers of Buchan, Aberdeenshire

SILVER IN THE WIND

The ptarmigan cries across the corrie,
sounds fading again in the grip of icy wind
that races fast on cliff wall and lichened gully;
beloved mountain, the wind blows silver,
there is silver in the wind.

A solitary hind, watchful, scans the ridge,
then, in silence, becomes invisible, stealing away from sight
to appear again, silhouetted on the crest, then to vanish;
mist on the mountain, the wind blows silver,
there is silver in the wind.

Where the timid adder sleeps, a fox moves, gliding,
skirting scree, above the loch, the surface still and frozen,
the air fills, as flakes carry from pinnacle to corrie wall;
mountain of snow, the wind blows silver,
there is silver in the wind.

Soon the peak lies below a white mantle,
snow cornices lining ragged rims, the climber turns away,
descending to seek protection in sheltered rocks;
mountain of storms, the wind blows silver,
there is silver in the wind.

IAN STRACHAN

Facing page: Creag na Caillich, Tarmachan Ridge, Perthshire

Loch Eilt and Ben Nevis, Lochaber

HADDOCK FISHERMEN

*M*idnight. The wind yawing nor-east.
A low blunt moon.
Unquiet beside quiet wives we rest.

A spit of rain and a gull
In the open door.
The lit fire. A quick mouthful of ale.

We push the *Merle* at a sea of cold flame
The oars drip honey.
Hook by hook uncoils under The Kame.

Our line breaks the trek of sudden thousands.
Twelve nobbled jaws,
Gray cowls, gape in our hands.

Twelve cold mouths scream without sound.
The sea is empty again.
Like tinkers the bright ones endlessly shift their ground.

We probe emptiness all the afternoon,
Then pause and fill our teeth
With dependable food, beef and barley scone.

Sunset drags its butcher blade
From the day's throat.
We turn through an ebb salt and sticky as blood.

More stars than fish. Women, cats, a gull
Mewl at the rock.
The valley divides the meagre miracle.

GEORGE MACKAY BROWN

IN THE HIGHLANDS

In the highlands, in the country places,
Where the old plain men have rosy faces,
And the young fair maidens
    Quiet eyes;
Where essential silence cheers and blesses,
And for ever in the hill-recesses
Her more lovely music
    Broods and dies.

O to mount again where erst I haunted;
Where the old red hills are bird-enchanted,
And the low green meadows
    Bright with sward;
And when even dies, the million-tinted,
And the night has come, and planets glinted,
Lo, the valley hollow
    Lamp-bestarred!

O to dream, O to awake and wander
There, and with delight to take and render,
Through the trance of silence
    Quiet breath;
Lo! for there, among the flowers and grasses,
Only the mightier movement sounds and passes;
Only winds and river,
    Life and death.

ROBERT LOUIS STEVENSON

Right: Highland loch

CHANGE AND IMMUTABILITY

*W*hen I went up to Clova glen
　　And I was in my 'teens
And got there on a bicycle
　　And lived on bread and beans
And covered twenty miles or so
　　And got up Dreish and Mayar
The May month oystercatcher flights
　　Were madly piping there.

When I went up to Clova glen
　　And I was fifty-five,
And lived on wine and caviare
　　And had a car to drive.
And managed half a dozen miles
　　And halfway up the hill
The May month oystercatcher flights
　　Were madly piping still.

SYD SCROGGIE

Facing page: Glen Clova, Angus

THE WILDERNESS

I came too late to the hills: they were swept bare
Winters before I was born of song and story,
Of spell or speech with power of oracle or invocation,

The great ash long dead by a roofless house, its branches rotten,
The voice of the crows an inarticulate cry,
And from the wells and springs the holy water ebbed away.

A child I ran in the wind on a withered moor
Crying out after those great presences who were not there,
Long lost in the forgetfulness of the forgotten.

Only the archaic forms themselves could tell
In sacred speech of hoodie on gray stone, or hawk in air,
Of Eden where the lonely rowan bends over the dark pool.

Yet I have glimpsed the bright mountain behind the mountain,
Knowledge under the leaves, tasted the bitter berries red,
Drunk water cold and clear from an inexhaustible hidden fountain.

KATHLEEN RAINE

Facing page: Lochan na Carnaich, Glenfinnan, Inverness-shire

76
~

SCOTLAND THE BRAVE

Hark when the night is falling,
Hear! hear the pipes are calling,
Loudly and proudly calling,
Down thro' the glen.
There where the hills are sleeping,
Now feel the blood a-leaping,
High as the spirits of the old Highland men.

Chorus
Towering in gallant fame,
Scotland my mountain hame,
High may your proud standards gloriously wave,
Land of my high endeavour,
Land of the shining river,
Land of my heart for ever,
Scotland the brave.

High in the misty Highlands
Out by the purple islands,
Brave are the hearts that beat
Beneath Scottish skies.
Wild are the winds to meet you,
Staunch are the friends that greet you,
Kind as the love that shines from fair maidens' eyes.

Far off in sunlit places
Sad are the Scottish faces,
Yearning to feel the kiss
Of sweet Scottish rain.
Where the tropics are beaming
Love sets the heart a-dreaming,
Longing and dreaming for the hameland again.

ANONYMOUS

The Rob Roy statue, Stirling

BRIGHT IS THE RING OF WORDS ...

*B*right is the ring of words
When the right man rings them,
Fair the fall of songs
When the singer sings them.
Still they are carolled and said –
On wings they are carried –
After the singer is dead
And the maker buried.

Low as the singer lies
In the field of heather,
Songs of his fashion bring
The swains together.
And when the west is red
With the sunset embers,
The lover lingers and sings
And the maid remembers.

ROBERT LOUIS STEVENSON

Facing page: Heather hillside

THE PAPS OF JURA

Before I crossed the sound
    I saw how from the sea
These breasts rise soft and round,
    Not two but three;

Now, climbing, I clasp rocks
    Storm-shattered and sharp-edged,
Grey ptarmigan their flocks,
    With starved moss wedged;

And mist like hair hangs over
    One barren breast and me,
Who climb, a desperate lover,
    With hand and knee.

ANDREW YOUNG

Right: the Paps of Jura and
the Sound of Islay, Inner Hebrides

HIGHLAND LOVES

Can one love a boulder
gritted and grey
and in the normal way
perched on the shoulder
of some obscure hill,
with heather shoots,
tiny and still,
peeping out from
crevice and crack and
adding soft colour to
unchanging rock?

Can one love the rain
marching in lances
across the tops
until light changes and
the swishing drops
alter the stones,
and amid dull hues yellow
lichen flashes and green
moss and amber tones
of different veins are
freshly embossed?

Can one love the birds,
brown, quick and small
with their darting flight
and piping calls
until by some trait of
movement or mark
they become known
like friends and
thus identified help
to captivate our
moorland hearts?

Can one love a tree
like this solitary birch,
judged as 'a weed'
and thereby besmirched
by those who do not know
its blinding beauty
against dwindling snow
and are unaware that it
cannot be 'classified'
but is love itself
realised.

RENNIE McOWAN

Facing page: Silver birch

HIGHLAND MARY

*Y*e banks and braes and streams around
   The castle o' Montgomery,
Green be your woods, and fair your flowers,
   Your waters never drumlie!
There simmer first unfauld her robes,
   And there the langest tarry;
For there I took the last fareweel
   O' my sweet Highland Mary.

How sweetly bloomed the gay green birk,
   How rich the hawthorn's blossom,
As underneath their fragrant shade
   I clasped her to my bosom!
The golden hours on angel wings
   Flew o'er me and my dearie;
For dear to me as light and life
   Was my sweet Highland Mary.

Wi' monie a vow and locked embrace
   Our parting was fu' tender;
And, pledging aft to meet again,
   We tore oursels asunder;
But oh! fell Death's untimely frost,
   That nipt my flower sae early!
Now green's the sod, and cauld's the clay,
   That wraps my Highland Mary!

O pale, pale now, those rosy lips
   I aft hae kissed sae fondly!
And closed for aye the sparkling glance
   That dwelt on me sae kindly!
And mouldering now in silent dust
   That heart that lo'ed me dearly!
But still within my bosom's core
   Shall live my Highland Mary.

ROBERT BURNS

Above: Hawthorn hedgerow

HUNTED

The wind on this bright sky-washed day
Tears words from my mouth, tossing them
Soundless after heedless red-coat children
Who bounce over the dry turf of the hill.

Suddenly, ears caught, startled
From its shelter in reedy hollow
Out of wind – 'Look, Daddy, look!' –
The brown hare comes erect,

Leaps the stream, angles left and right
Through gorse and bracken, and steeples sharply
Up the hillside, big-footed. He pauses
Once (no dog at his heels bites

Or snarls) looking back upon his hapless
Round-eyed hunters. I can see
His muscles tremble, heart thumping
At ribs, his death in our footfall.

KEN MORRICE

Facing page: Hare in winter

DEER AT THE ROADSIDE

*Y*esterday three deer stood at the roadside.
It was icy January and there they were
like debutantes on a smooth ballroom floor.

They stared at us out of that French
arrogant atmosphere, like Louis the Sixteenth
sustained in twilight on a marble plinth.

They wore the inhuman look of aristocrats
before a revolution comes, and the people
blaspheme the holy bells in the high steeple.

So were these deer, balanced on delicate logic,
till suddenly they broke from us and went
outraged and sniffing into the dark wind.

Difficult to say where they go to
in the harsh weather when the mountains stand
like judging elders, tall on either hand.

Except that they know the ice is breaking now.
They take to the hills pursued by darkness and lie
beneath the starry metaphysical sky.

Sometimes in a savage winter they'll come down
and beg like fallen nobles for their bread.
They'd rather live in poverty than be dead.

Nevertheless there's something dangerous
in a deer's head. He might suddenly open your belly
with his bitter antlers to the barren sky.

Red deer stag

Especially in winter when tormented
by loneliness they descend to this road
with great bounding leaps like the mind of God.

(FROM DEER ON THE HIGH HILLS – A MEDITATION)
IAIN CRICHTON SMITH

I KNOW NOT HOW IT IS WITH YOU ...

I know not how it is with you –
I loved the first and last,
The whole field of the present view,
The whole flow of the past.

One tittle of the things that are
Nor you should change nor I –
One pebble in our path – one star
In all our heaven of sky.

Our lives, and every day and hour,
One symphony appear:
One road, one garden – every flower
And every bramble dear.

ROBERT LOUIS STEVENSON

Facing page: Periwinkles

LOCH OSSIAN

It was a heat to melt the mountains in,
The basking adder sunned his varnished span
And cooled the burning rock beneath his skin.
The aromatic resin swelled and ran;
Whilst, in the arid timber, tall and still,
Each needle nodded in the larch's shade:
And, bare above its plaid, the shapely hill
Seemed as the sunburnt shoulders of a maid,
Shyly disrobing by the shore alone.
Loch Ossian looked its very loveliest,
With lazing water warm against the stone,
The heron silent in his island nest,
And such a golden langour through the haze
That Summer seemed in love with idle days.

SYD SCROGGIE

Right: Lochside pines

HORSE

The horse at the shore
Casks of red apples, skull, a barrel of rum

The horse in the field
Plough, ploughman, gulls, a furrow, a cornstalk

The horse in the peat-bog
Twelve baskets of dark fire

The horse at the pier
Letters, bread, paraffin, one passenger, papers

The horse at the show
Ribbons, raffia, high bright hooves

The horse in the meadow
A stallion, a red wind, between the hills

The horse at the burn
Quenching a long flame in the throat

GEORGE MACKAY BROWN

Right: Eildon Hills, Selkirkshire

THE BANKS O' DOON

Ye banks and braes o' bonnie Doon,
    How can ye bloom sae fresh and fair;
How can ye chant, ye little birds,
    And I sae weary, fu' o' care!
Thou'll break my heart, thou warbling bird
    That wantons thro' the flowering thorn:
Thou minds me o' departed joys,
    Departed, never to return.

Aft hae I rov'd by bonnie Doon,
    To see the rose and woodbine twine;
And ilka bird sang o' its luve,
    And fondly sae did I o' mine;
Wi' lightsome heart I pu'd a rose,
    Fu' sweet upon its thorny tree;
And my fause luver stole my rose,
    But, ah! he left the thorn wi' me.

ROBERT BURNS

Facing page: The River Doon near
Straitton, Ayrshire

SCOTLAND SMALL?

*S*cotland small? Our multiform, our infinite Scotland *small*?
Only as a patch of hillside may be a cliché corner
To a fool that cries 'Nothing but heather!' Where in September another
Sitting there and resting and gazing round
Sees not only heather but blaeberries
With bright green leaves and leaves already turned scarlet,
Hiding ripe blue berries; and amongst the sage-green leaves
Of the bog myrtle the golden flowers of tormentil shining;
And on the small bare places, where the little Blackface sheep
Found grazing, milkworts blue as summer skies;
And down in neglected peat-hags, not worked
In living memory, sphagnum moss in pastel shades
Of yellow, green, and pink; sundew and butterwort
And nodding harebells vying in their colour
With blue butterflies that poise themselves delicately upon them.
And stunted rowans with harsh dry leaves of glorious colour
'Nothing but heather!' – How marvellously descriptive! And incomplete!

HUGH MACDIARMID

Facing page: Common Blue butterfly

TO S.R. CROCKET

Blows the wind today, and the sun and rain are flying,
Blows the wind on the moors today and now,
Where about the graves of the martyrs and whaups are crying,
My heart remembers now!

Grey recumbent tombs of the dead in desert places,
Standing stones on the vacant wine-red moor,
Hills of sheep, and the howes of the silent vanished races,
And winds, austere and pure.

Be it granted to me to behold you again in dying,
Hills of home! and to hear again the call;
Hear about the graves of the martyrs the peewees crying,
And hear no more at all.

ROBERT LOUIS STEVENSON

Facing page: Rowan in autumn

Ettrick Valley from Ashkirk, Selkirkshire

THE ROAD TO ROBERTON

The hill road to Roberton: Ale Water at our feet,
And grey hills and blue hills that melt away and meet,
With cotton-flowers that wave to us and lone whaups that call,
And over all the Border mist – the soft mist over all.

When Scotland married England long, long ago,
The winds spun a wedding veil of moonlight and snow,
A veil of filmy silver that sun and rain had kissed,
And she left it to the Border in a soft grey mist.

And now the dreary distance doth wear it like a bride,
Out beyond the Langhope Burn and over Essenside,
By Borthwick Wa's and Redfordgreen and on to wild Buccleuch
And up the Ettrick Water, till it fades into the blue.

The winding road to Roberton is little marked of wheels,
And lonely past Blawearie runs the track to Borthwickshiels,
Whitslade is slumbering undisturbed and down in Harden Glen
The tall trees murmur in their dreams of Wat's mosstrooping men.

A distant glint of silver, that is Ale's last goodbye,
Then Greatmoor and Windburgh against a purple sky,
The long line of the Carter, Teviotdale flung wide,
And a slight stir in the heather – a wind from the English side.

The hill road to Roberton's a steep road to climb,
But where your foot has crushed it you can smell the scented thyme,
And if your heart's a Border heart, look down to Harden Glen,
And hear the blue hills ringing with the restless hoofs again.

WILL H. OGILVIE

105

THE SKYE BOAT SONG

Chorus

Speed bonnie boat like a bird on the wing,
Onward, the sailors cry.
Carry the lad that's born to be king
Over the sea to Skye.

Loud the winds howl, loud the waves roar,
Thunderclaps rend the air,
Baffled, our foes stand by the shore,
Follow they will not dare.

Though the waves leap, soft shall ye sleep,
Ocean's a royal bed.
Rock'd in the deep, Flora will keep
Watch o'er your weary head.

Many's the lad fought on that day,
Well the claymore could wield,
When the night came, silently lay
Dead on Culloden's field.

Burned are our homes, exile and death,
Scattered the loyal men;
Yet ere the sword cool in the sheath,
Charlie will come again.

HAROLD BOULTON

Right: Sound of Sleat and the Isle of Skye,
Inner Hebrides

ST NINIAN'S ISLE

*A*nd in the morning there is the
slow peristalsis of the sea and the
white bones on the beach, like a huge
sprawling corpse had died there on the white sands.
And all the gods had passed that way
leaving on the green island a pile of silver
brooches and buckles engraved perhaps with a devil's mask.

You see a gull fall from its mast
of blue sky, has that same face, the same
quick beak that grasps the thick trout
or breaks the mussel's back on a rock,
as the monks must have done in the
past; hammering

Out the face from the silver's black;
they conquered their fear by making
it useful; selling to the tourists from
their small stocks, but keeping the best
for themselves, held back the fear they had
when coming from the west, from which they
could not turn back.

And here the remnants of that golden age
an island unchanged; a latitude marked
by one of the old sixareens hauling from the deeps;
the houses smoking on the curve of the bay;
the black peat stacks straining in their lines –

And we too hold back that golden age like
the gull that swoops and screams
when it finds the bones are picked
clean and only the sea's whites and greens remain.

JAMES RANKIN

Facing page: St Ninian's Isle, Shetland

AT EUSTON

*S*tranger with the pile of luggage proudly labelled for Portree,
How I wish, this night of August, I were you and you were me!
Think of all that lies before you when the train goes sliding forth
And the lines athwart the sunset lead you swiftly to the North!
Think of breakfast at Kingussie, think of high Drumochter Pass,
Think of Highland breezes singing through the bracken and the grass,
Scabious blue and yellow daisy, tender fern beside the train,
Rowdy Tummel falling, brawling, seen and lost and glimpsed again!
You will pass my golden roadway of the days of long ago;
Will you realise the magic of the names I used to know:
Clachnaharry, Achnashellach, Achnasheen, and Duirinish?
Ev'ry moor alive with coveys, ev'ry pool aboil with fish?
Ev'ry well-remembered vista more exciting mile by mile
Till the wheeling gulls are screaming round the engine at the Kyle.
Think of cloud on Bheinn na Cailleach, jagged Cuchullins soaring high,
Scent of peat and all the glamour of the misty Isle of Skye!

A.M. HARBORD

Facing page: Steam train at Lochailort, Inverness-shire

A MAN'S A MAN FOR A' THAT

Is there for honest poverty
That hings his head, and a' that?
The coward slave, we pass him by –
We dare be poor, for a' that!
For a' that, and a' that!
Our toils obscure, and a' that.
The rank is but the guinea's stamp,
The man's the gowd, for a' that.

What though on hamely fare we dine,
Wear hodden grey and a' that?
Gie fools their silks, and knaves their wine –
A man's a man, for a' that.
For a' that and a' that.
Their tinsel show, and a' that,
The honest man, though e'er sae poor,
Is king o' men for a' that.

Then let us pray that come it may
(As come it will for a' that)
That Sense and Worth o'er all the earth
Shall bear the gree and a' that!
For a' that comin' yet for a' that,
That man to man, the world o'er,
Shall brothers be for a' that.

ROBERT BURNS

Facing page: Stained glass, St Conans,
Loch Awe, Argyllshire

LOVE IN AGE

*N*ow that we have had our day, you
having carried, borne children,
been responsible through the wearing years,
in this moment and the next
and still the next as our love
spreads to tomorrow's horizon,
we talk a little before silence.

Let the young make up their love songs,
about which subject they are securely ignorant.
Let them look into eyes that mirror
themselves. Let them groan and ululate
their desire into a microphone. Let them
shout their proclamations over the tannoy
– a whisper is enough for us.

GEORGE BRUCE

Right: Evening at Arisaig, Argyllshire

JOHN ANDERSON, MY JO

John Anderson, my jo, John,
   When we were first acquent,
Your locks were like the raven,
   Your bonnie brow was brent;
But now your brow is beld, John,
   Your locks are like the snaw;
But blessings on your frosty pow,
   John Anderson, my jo.

John Anderson, my jo, John,
   We clamb the hill thegither;
And mony a canty day, John,
   We've had wi' ane anither;
Now we maun totter down, John:
   And hand in hand we'll go,
And sleep thegither at the foot,
   John Anderson, my jo.

ROBERT BURNS

Left: Lochalsh woodland garden,
Inverness-shire

NO ACCIDENT

*W*alking downhill from Suilven (a fine day, for once)
I twisted a knee. Two crippling miles to walk.
Leap became lower. Bag swung from a bowed neck.
Pedant of walking learned it like a dunce.

I didn't mind so much. Suilven's a place
That gives more than a basket of trout. It opens
The space it lives in and a heaven's revealed, in
                                    glimpses.
Grace is a crippling thing. You've to pay for grace.

The heaven's an odd one, shaped like cliff and scree
No less than they are: no picnicking place, but hiding
Forevers and everywheres in every thing – including
A two-mile walk, even, and a crippled knee.

You reach it by revelation. Good works can't place
Heaven in a dead hind and a falcon going
Or in the hard truth that, if only by being
First in a lower state, you've to pay for grace.

NORMAN MACCAIG

Right: Loch Veyatie and Suilven, Sutherland

SCOTLAND

Here in the uplands
The soil is ungrateful
The fields, red with sorrel,
    Are stony and bare.
A few trees, wind-twisted –
Or are they but bushes?
Stand stubbornly guarding
    A home here and there.

Scooped out like a saucer,
The land lies before me;
The waters, once scattered,
    Flow orderly now
Through fields where the ghosts
Of the marsh and the moorland
Still ride the old marches,
    Despising the plough.

The marsh and the moorland
Are not to be banished;
The bracken and heather,
    The glory of broom,
Usurp all the balks
And the field's broken fringes,
And claim from the sower
    Their portion of room.

This is my country,
The land that begat me,
These windy spaces
    Are surely my own.
And those who here toil
In the sweat of their faces
Are flesh of my flesh,
    And bone of my bone.

Hard is the day's task
Scotland, stern Mother –
Wherewith at all times
    Thy sons have been faced:
Labour by day,
And scant rest in the gloaming
With Want an attendant,
    Not lightly outpaced.

Yet do thy children
Honour and love thee.
Harsh is thy schooling,
    Yet great is the gain:
True hearts and strong limbs,
The beauty of faces,
Kissed by the wind
    And caressed by the rain.

ALEXANDER GRAY

Facing page: Working the peat

THE EMIGRANT

When I stood on the breast of the hill,
    Looking down on my native glen,
On the woods, and burns, and the wee white roads
    I never would see again,
My heart was so laden with grief,
    That my eyes were blinded with tears,
For there were the scenes of a thousand joys
    Of my light, young years.

The morning was soft and still,
    And the last of my kith and kin
Lay under the sod in the cold clay earth,
    Old, grey-headed and thin;
Oh! the glen was so solemn and quiet,
    Not even a bird gave tongue;
And yet on a day there was laughter and dance,
    And the merry song.

The clothes that I wore were poor;
    The shoes on my feet were thin;
The bundle I carried was light on my back,
    With all that I owned therein;
I was going from hunger away,
    To a land that promised me bread,
But I could not sing with the hopes to be,
    For my heart was dead.

Facing page: Parallel roads, Glen Roy, Inverness-shire

I stood on the breast of the hill
  Looking down through a mist of pain,
On the woods, and burns, and the wee white roads
  I never would see again.
Then softly I said, 'Farewell!'
  And I turned my face to the west;
But well I knew that the promised land
  Would bring no rest.

JOE CORBIE

THE FINISHED HOUSE

In the finished house, a flame is brought to the hearth.
Then a table, between door and window
Where a stranger will eat before the men of the house.
A bed is laid in a secret corner
For the three agonies – love, birth, death –
That are made beautiful with ceremony.
The neighbours come with gifts –
A set of cups, a calendar, some chairs,
A fiddle is hung at the wall.
A girl puts lucky salt in a dish.
The cupboard has its loaf and bottle.
On the seventh morning
One spills water of blessing over the threshold.

GEORGE MACKAY BROWN

Left: Burns Cottage interior,
Alloway, Ayrshire

BREATHES THERE THE
MAN ...

Breathes there the man with soul so dead,
  Who never to himself hath said,
   This is my own, my native land!
Whose heart hath ne'er within him burn'd,
As home his footsteps he hath turn'd
   From wandering on a foreign strand! –
If such there breathe, go, mark him well;
For him no Minstrel raptures swell;
High though his titles, proud his name;
Boundless his wealth as wish can claim;
Despite those titles, power, and pelf,
The wretch, concentrated all in self,
Living, shall forfeit fair renown,
And, doubly dying, shall go down
To the vile dust, from whence he sprung,
Unwept, unhonour'd, and unsung.

SIR WALTER SCOTT

Right: Scott's view of the
Eildon Hills, Selkirkshire

THE THINGS OF THE NORTH

*L*et us give thanks for the things of the north ...
    For blue, distant mountains tipping the curving brown sweep of moorland,
    for grey, drystane walls climbing the green shoulder of a sunlit hill,
    for hardy white houses, low-slung against the winds as if they had
        taken root,
    for scattered clinging woods and storm-bent trees telling of strength
        and solitude.

Let us give thanks for the things of the north ...
    For dusty roads running to quiet farms deep in the glens,
    for lichened stones and hidden lochs placid beneath the cliffs,
    for amber burns that wend a gentle way though white bog-cotton
    for all the silences that so delight and the clean scents of a Highland night.

Let us give thanks for the things of the north ...
    For winds and rain that scour endless miles of rippling heather,
    for an elemental wildness that knows little of cities and towns,
    for an understanding that in stark harshness blinding beauty there abounds
    for those who walk and seek and find.

Let us give thanks for the things of the north.

RENNIE McOWAN

Facing page: Autumn mist in the Tay Valley, Perthshire

LEWIS IN SUMMER

*T*he atmosphere clear and transparent
as though the veil had been rent
and the Creator were sitting in full view of His people
eating potatoes and herring,
with no man to whom He can say grace.
Probably there's no other sky in the world
that makes it so easy for people
to look in on eternity;
you don't need philosophy
where you can make do with binoculars.

DERICK THOMSON

Left: Isle of Lewis, Outer Hebrides

SCOTLAND'S WINTER

Now the ice lays its smooth claws on the sill,
The sun looks from the hill
Helmed in his winter casket,
And sweeps his arctic sword across the sky.
The water at the mill
Sounds more hoarse and dull.
The miller's daughter walking by
With frozen fingers soldered to her basket
Seems to be knocking
Upon a hundred leagues of floor
With her light heels, and mocking
Percy and Douglas dead,
And Bruce on his burial bed,
Where he lies white as may
With wars and leprosy,
And all the kings before
This land was kingless
And all the singers before
This land was songless,
This land that with its dead and living waits the Judgement Day.
But they, the powerless dead,
Listening can hear no more
Than a hard tapping on the sounding floor
A little overhead
Of common heels that do not know
Whence they come or where they go
And are content
With their poor frozen life and shallow banishment.

EDWIN MUIR

Right: Winter near Dalmally, Argyllshire

Lower Falls of the River Nevis, Lochaber

AFTON WATER

Flow gently, sweet Afton, among thy green braes,
Flow gently, I'll sing thee a song in thy praise;
My Mary's asleep by thy murmuring stream,
Flow gently, sweet Afton, disturb not her dream.

Thou stock-dove whose echo resounds thro' the glen,
Ye wild whistling blackbirds in yon thorny den,
Thou green-crested lapwing, thy screaming forbear,
I charge you disturb not my slumbering fair.

How lofty, sweet Afton, thy neighbouring hills,
Far marked with the courses of clear winding rills;
There daily I wander as noon rises high,
My flocks and my Mary's sweet cot in my eye.

How pleasant thy banks and green valleys below,
Where wild in the woodlands the primroses blow;
There oft as mild ev'ning weeps over the lea,
The sweet-scented birk shades my Mary and me.

Thy crystal stream, Afton, how lovely it glides,
And winds by the cot where my Mary resides;
How wanton thy waters her snowy feet lave,
As gathering sweet flow'rets she stems thy clear wave.

Flow gently, sweet Afton, among thy green braes,
Flow gently, sweet river, the theme of my lays;
My Mary's asleep by thy murmuring stream,
Flow gently, sweet Afton, disturb not her dream.

ROBERT BURNS

INDEX OF FIRST LINES

INDEX OF POEMS

ACKNOWLEDGEMENTS

Grateful acknowledgement is made to the following for permission to reprint the poems in this book.
All possible care has been made to trace ownership of selections and to make full acknowledgement.
If any errors or omissions have occurred, they will be corrected in subsequent editions,
provided that notification is sent to the publisher.

James Aitchison: *Princes Street Gardens*, by kind permission of the author
Marion Angus: *Anemones*, from *The Singin' Lass* by permission of Faber and Faber, London
Harold Boulton: *The Skye Boat Song*, by permisson of Cramer Music, London
George Bruce: *Love in Age*; *The Fisherman*, by kind permission of the author
Stewart Conn: *The Clearing*; *Todd*, by kind permission of the author
Joe Corbie: *The Emigrant*, by kind permission of Morag Corrie
Iain Crichton Smith: *Deer at the Roadside*; *Highland Portrait*, from *Collected Poems* by permission of
Carcanet Press, Manchester
Douglas Fraser: *Freedom of the Hills*; *On Looking at an Old Climbing Photograph*, by kind
permission of Mrs H. Moncur
G.S. Fraser: *The Traveller Has Regrets*, by kind permission of Eileen Fraser
Alexander Gray: *Scotland*, by kind permission of John Gray
A.M. Harbord: *At Euston*, by permission of *The Tatler and Bystander*, London
Maurice Lindsay: *Highland Shooting Lodge*, by kind permission of the author
Norman MacCaig: *No accident*; *Sun blink*, from *Collected Poems* by permission of
Random House UK, London
Hugh MacDiarmid: *Scotland Small?* from *Collected Poems* by permission of Carcanet Press, Manchester
George Mackay Brown: *Trout Fisher* and *Haddock Fishermen* from *Selected Poems*; *Horse* and *The Finished
House* from *Scottish Poetry One* by permission of John Murray (Publishers) Ltd., London
Rennie McOwan: *Highland Loves*; *The Things of the North*, by kind permission of the author
Edwin Morgan: *Strawberries*, from *Collected Poems* by permission of Carcanet Press, Manchester
Ken Morrice: *Hunted*, by kind permission of the author
Edwin Muir: *A Birthday*; *Scotland's Winter*; *The Sufficient Place*, from *Collected Poems* by permission of
Faber and Faber, London
Kathleen Raine: *The Wilderness*, by kind permission of the author
James Rankin: *St Ninian's Isle*, by kind permission of the author
Syd Scroggie: *Change and Immutability*; *Loch Ossian*, by kind permission of the author
William Souter: *The Permanence of the Young Men*, from *Collected Poems* by permission of the Trustees of
the National Library of Scotland
Muriel Stuart: *The Wood and the Shore*, from *Selected Poems* by permission of Random House UK, London
Derick Thomson: *Lewis in Summer*; *The Island*, by kind permission of the author
Ruthven Todd: *Watching You Walk*, from *Garland for the Winter Solstice* by permission of David Higham
Associates, London
Sydney Tremayne: *The Falls of Falloch*, from *Time and the Wind*, published by Collins. Copyright © 1948
by permission of Sheil Land Associates Ltd, London
Andrew Young: *Loch Brandy*; *The Mountain*; *The Paps of Jura*; *The Falls of Glomach*, from *The Poetical
Works of Andrew Young*, ed. Lowbury & Young, (Secker & Warburg, 1985) by permission of Alison Young
Douglas Young: *For the Old Highlands*, by permission of the Saltire Society, Ayr

The editor would like to offer her personal thanks to George Bruce and Stewart Conn for their help, and
to Elizabeth MacGregor, Assistant Librarian at the Scottish Poetry Library, for her research.
Bob Lawson at Scotland in Focus deserves a special acknowledgement for his
generous assistance with the choice of photographs.